ST. ALDHELM'S RESOURCE CENTRE A 3
EDGEWARE ROAD,
SWINDON.
0793 491065

Infants

copy 1
0044

The Bear facts

Teddy Horsley books are designed to build bridges between the young child's day to day experiences of the world and major biblical themes and stories.

Both authors work in church-linked colleges concerned with Teacher Education. Nicola Slee lectures in Religious Studies at Whitelands College in London. Leslie Francis is Research Fellow at Trinity College in Carmarthen.

Laura Cooper is a freelance children's illustrator working from Bristol. She has been engaged in art amongst groups of children and mentally handicapped adults.

The Teddy Horsley Series is a result of the authors' wide experience of educational work in schools and churches, and their extensive research into the religious development of young children.

"A Day With Teddy Horsley" has previously been published as three separate stories:
Good Morning   The Grumpy Day   Night Time

BIBLE SOCIETY
Stonehill Green, Westlea, SWINDON SN5 7DG, England
Series editor: David Martin
Text © Leslie J Francis and Nicola M Slee 1990
Illustrations © Bible Society 1990

Unless otherwise stated, quotations from the Bible Societies/Harper Collins © American Bible Society, New York, 1966, 1971, 1976.

A catalogue record for this book is available from the British Library

This edition published 1992. ISBN 0 564 081957. Printed in Hong Kong.

Good Morning

Teddy Horsley learns to be Thankful

When he wakes up Teddy Horsley likes to peep through his bedroom window.

Some mornings, the sun is shining warmly over the roof tops.

Teddy Horsley puts on his sun-glasses.

He goes paddling in the pool with Lucy, Walter, and Betsy Bear

and they all enjoy large ice-creams.

Teddy Horsley says thank you for the sun.

Some mornings, the rain is beating heavily on the windows.

Teddy Horsley pulls on his waterproof boots.

He goes splashing in the puddles with Lucy, Walter, and Betsy Bear.

They all enjoy singing under their umbrella.

Teddy Horsley says thank you for the rain.

Some mornings, the wind is blowing fiercely through the trees.

Teddy Horsley pulls down his woolly hat.

He goes walking in the town with Lucy, Walter, and Betsy Bear

and they all enjoy being blown along the street.

Teddy Horsley says thank you for the wind.

Some mornings, the frost is sparkling brightly on the lawn.

Teddy Horsley wraps round his warm scarf.

He goes sliding in the park with Lucy, Walter, and Betsy Bear.

They all enjoy steaming mugs of soup.

Teddy Horsley says thank you for the frost.

When he wakes up, Teddy Horsley likes to say thank you to God.

In *Good Morning*, Teddy Horsley enjoys a sunny day, a rainy day, a windy day, and a frosty day. Through these very different experiences he learns to thank God "in all circumstances" and to fulfil Paul's teaching to the Thessalonians in 1 Thessalonians 5:

Be joyful always, pray at all times, be thankful in all circumstances. This is what God wants from you...
1 Thessalonians 5.16-18.

The following questions suggest further ways of developing the links between the young child's experience, the story, and the Bible passage.

Talk about what you like doing:
What do you like doing on a sunny morning?
What do you like doing on a rainy morning?
What do you like doing on a windy morning?
What do you like doing on a frosty morning?

Talk about the story:
What did Teddy Horsley do when the sun shone?
What did Teddy Horsley do when it rained?
What did Teddy Horsley do when the wind blew?
What did Teddy Horsley do when it was frosty?
Why did Teddy Horsley say thank you?

Think some more about the story:
What is the weather like today?
What do you think Teddy Horsley might do on a day like today?
What might he say thank you for today?
How would he say thank you?

Think about the Bible passage:
What has made you happy today?
How do you say thank you?
What makes people happy?
How do they say thank you?
How do people say thank you to God?

The Grumpy Day

Teddy Horsley learns about Forgiveness

It is Monday morning and Teddy Horsley is a grumpy bear.

Teddy Horsley wakes up early when Walter turns up his radio.

Walter says sorry, but Teddy Horsley throws his pillow at him.

Teddy Horsley spills his drink when Betsy Bear bumps into the table.

Betsy Bear says sorry, but Teddy Horsley trips her up.

Teddy Horsley has to wait outside the bathroom when Lucy washes her hair.

Lucy says sorry, but Teddy Horsley bangs loudly on the door.

Teddy Horsley slips on the wet floor when Mrs Henry washes it.

Mrs Henry says sorry, but Teddy Horsley kicks her bucket.

Teddy Horsley falls over the cleaner when Mr Henry leaves it on the mat.

Mr Henry says sorry, but Teddy Horsley stamps his feet.

Teddy Horsley suddenly sees what a grumpy bear he is

and says sorry to Mr and Mrs Henry, Lucy, Walter, and Betsy Bear.

Walter picks up the pillow and puts it on Teddy Horsley's bed.

Betsy Bear makes Teddy Horsley another drink and brings it to the table.

Lucy hurries in the bathroom and leaves it tidy for Teddy Horsley.

46

Mrs Henry dries the floor to make it safe.

Mr Henry puts the cleaner away in the cupboard.

Teddy Horsley knows that Mr and Mrs Henry, Lucy, Walter, and Betsy Bear forgive him.

Teddy Horsley sees what a naughty bear he has been

and says sorry to God for being so grumpy.

Teddy Horsley knows that God forgives him too.

In *The Grumpy Day,* Teddy Horsley forgives Mr and Mrs Henry, Lucy, Walter, and Betsy Bear and receives forgiveness from them. He learns to say sorry to God and knows he receives God's forgiveness, too. These experiences bring alive Jesus' teaching to the disciples about how to pray in Matthew 6:

Jesus said, "this, then, is how you should pray...
'Forgive us the wrongs we have done
as we forgive the wrongs that
others have done to us.'
Matthew 6. 9, 12.

The following questions suggest further ways of developing the links between the young child's experience, story, and the Bible passage.

Talk about what makes you grumpy:
When do you get grumpy?
What makes you grumpy?
When do you say sorry?

Talk about the story:
What did Teddy Horsley do to Walter?
What did Teddy Horsley do to Betsy Bear?
What did Teddy Horsley do to Lucy?
What did Teddy Horsley do to Mrs Henry?
What did Teddy Horsley do to Mr Henry?
Why did Teddy Horsley say sorry to his family?
Why did Teddy Horsley say sorry to God?

Think some more about the story:
What other things might make Teddy Horsley grumpy?
What might he do?
How might he say sorry?

Think about the Bible passage:
What have you done today?
Who has made you grumpy?
How can you forgive them?
Who have you made unhappy today?
How can you say sorry to them?
How do people say sorry to God?

Night Time

Teddy Horsley feels safe at Night

Night has come and Teddy Horsley is going to bed.

He pushes open his bedroom door to peep inside.

Then he sees something stir in the corner and dark shadows play on the walls.

When Mr and Mrs Henry switch on the lamp the shadows
disappear

and Teddy Horsley sees the sleepy cat stretch in the corner.

He picks up his toys to put them in the cupboard.

Then he sees something hiding under the bed.

When Mr and Mrs Henry lift up the bedspread Teddy Horsley laughs at his slippers lying there.

Teddy Horsley feels safe because Mr and Mrs Henry are with him in his bedroom.

He folds up his clothes to put them on the table.

Then he feels something move behind the curtains.

When he pulls the curtains back Teddy Horsley
finds the window open

and the cold night breeze is blowing in.

He peers through the window to look at the black night outside.

Then he hears frightening noises echo through the darkness.

He waves to the tawny owl hooting "goodnight".

Teddy Horsley feels safe because Mr and Mrs Henry are with him in the house.

Night has come and Teddy Horsley turns off the light.

He still sees shadows playing on the wall, but he is not afraid.

He still feels movement behind the curtain, but he is not afraid.

He still hears noises echo through the darkness, but he is not afraid.

Teddy Horsley feels safe because the Lord is with him through the night.

In *Night Time,* Teddy Horsley's experience of overcoming fears of the dark brings alive the confidence of Psalm 91:

The LORD will cover you with his wings;
you will be safe in his care;
his faithfulness will protect and defend you.
You need not fear any dangers at night
or sudden attacks during the day
or plagues that strike in the dark
or evils that kill in daylight.

You have made the LORD your defender,
the Most High your protector,
and so no disaster will strike you,
no violence will come near your home.
God will put his angels in charge of you
to protect you wherever you go.
Psalm 91.4-6, 9-11.

The following questions suggest further ways of developing the links between the bible passage and the young child's experience.

Talk about going to bed:
How do you get ready for bed?
Who helps you get ready for bed?
What things do you like to have near you at night?
Who do you like to have near you in the house when you go to bed?

Talk about the story:
What sights did Teddy Horsley see when he opened his bedroom door?
What did he discover when Mr and Mrs Henry switched on the light?
What movement did Teddy Horsley feel behind the curtains?
What did he discover when he pulled back the curtains
What sounds did Teddy Horsley hear in the darkness outside?
What did he discover when he looked harder?
How did Teddy Horsley feel when he turned off the light?
Why did he feel safe?

Think some more about the story:
What else might Teddy Horsley see in his bedroom at night?
What else might he feel in the darkness?
What else might he hear in the street outside?

Think about the Bible passage:

A psalm is a kind of song.

What night-time fears are described in the psalm?
What day-time dangers are described in the psalm?
How does God promise to protect us from the night-time fears and day-time dangers?

Also available in this series:
Out and About with Teddy Horsley:
The Walk   Explorer   Neighbours